Focus on
LITERACY

Starter Level
Read-along Book

Karina Law

Focus on Literacy Starter Level Read-along Book

First published 2001

© HarperCollins*Publishers* Ltd 2001

10 9 8 7 6 5 4 3 2

ISBN-13: 978 0 00 711100 8
ISBN-10: 0 00 711100 2

A catalogue record for this book is available from the British Library.

Published by Collins
A division of HarperCollins*Publishers* Ltd
77–85 Fulham Palace Road
London W6 8JB

www.**Collins**Education.com **On-line Support for Schools and Colleges**	www.**fire**and**water**.com Visit the book lover's website

Printed in Great Britain by Martins the Printers, Berwick upon Tweed

Author	Karina Law
Series Editors	Barry and Anita Scholes
Cover design	Grasshopper Design Company
Design	Ken Vail Graphic Design
Editor	Gaynor Spry
Cover image	Gary Hunter/Tony Stone Images
Illustrations	John Eastwood, Tim Etheridge, Ann Kronheimer, Bethan Matthews, Lisa Smith, Barbara Vagnozzi, Lisa Williams

Text, design and illustrations © HarperCollins*Publishers*
Ltd 2001.

Collins would like to thank Pat O'Brien and all at English
Martyrs RC Primary School, Liverpool.

Acknowledgements

The author and publishers wish to thank the following for
permission to use copyright material:

Hodder & Stoughton Limited for an extract of text and
illustrations from *Can Do* by Joyce Dunbar published by Simon
& Schuster Young Books; HarperCollins*Publishers* for an extract
of text and illustrations from *One Fish, Two Fish, Red Fish, Blue
Fish* by Dr. Seuss © 1960 Dr. Seuss; Candlewick Press inc,
Cambridge MA, and Rhoda Weyr Agency, NY for an extract of
text and illustrations from *What Is the Sun?* by Reeve
Lindbergh, illustrated by Stephen Lambert, text © 1994 Reeve
Lindbergh and Illustrations © 1994 Stephen Lambert; Scholastic
limited for "Keith's Cupboard" by Michael Rosen; The Watts
Publishing Group Limited for "O My Grand Old Grandpa York" by
Lucy Coats, from *First Rhymes* by Lucy Coats, first published in
the UK by Orchard Books in 1994, a division of The Watts
Publishing Group Limited, 96 Leonard Street, London EC2A
4XD; HarperCollins*Publishers* for "Wet Play" from *I Hear
Thunder* by David Orme; HarperCollins*Publishers* for an extract
of text and illustrations from *Catherine and the Lion* by Clare
Jarrett © Clare Jarrett 1996; Anderson Press Limited for an
extract of text and illustrations from *A Dark, Dark Tale* by Ruth
Brown; Mathew Price Children's Books for an extract of text and
illustrations from *The Baked Bean Queen* by Rose Impey,
illustrated by Sue Porter; The Agency (London) Limited for *It's
Time for Lunch, Rosie!* by Tony Bradman © Tony Bradman
1998, first published in *Toddler Playtime* by
HarperCollins*Publishers*, all rights reserved and enquiries to
The Agency (London) Limited, 24 Pottery lane, London W11
4LZ fax: 0207 727 9037; David Higham Associates Limited for
"Night Sounds" from *Walking on Air* by Berlie Doherty, published
by HarperCollins*Publishers*; Curtis Brown Group for "Early
Country Village Morning" by Grace Nichols from *Come into my
Tropical Garden* published by A & C Black; John Foster, for
"Here a Bear, There a Bear" by John Foster from *First Verses*
published by Oxford University Press © 1996 John Foster.

Every effort has been made to trace copyright holders
and to obtain their permission for the use of the copyright
material. The author and publishers will gladly receive any
information enabling them to rectify any error or omission in
subsequent editions.

Contents

Starter Level
Read-along Book

Can Do

I wish I could …
fly like a bird,
swim like a tadpole.
But I CAN'T!

What I CAN do is …
hop, skip, and jump.

I wish I could …
climb trees like my cat,
see into the bathroom mirror,
reach the biscuit tin.

But I CAN'T!
But I CAN slide
down the slide
at the park.

5

I wish I could …
whistle a tune,
spin a web like a spider,
catch a tooth fairy.

But I CAN'T!
But I CAN blow
big, shiny bubbles.

6

I wish I could …
count to a million,
write in straight lines,
read scary comics.
But I CAN'T!

But I CAN paint a lovely funny picture …
cut out paper chain people …
turn a head-over-heels …
get dressed all by myself.

So you see …
there are lots of things
I CAN DO!

By Joyce Dunbar

Ten Little Fingers

I have ten little fingers,
And they all belong to me.
I can make them do things.
Would you like to see?

I can shut them
up tight,

Or open them
all wide.

I can put them
all together,

Or make them
all hide.

I can make them
jump high,

I can make
them jump low,

I can fold
them quietly,
And sit just so.

Say!

Say!
Look at his fingers!
One, two, three …
How many fingers
do I see?

One, two, three, four,
five, six, seven,
eight, nine, ten.
He has eleven!

Eleven!
This is something new.
I wish I had
eleven, too!

By Dr. Seuss

Doctor Foster

Doctor Foster went to Gloucester,
in a shower of rain.
He stepped in a puddle,
right up to his middle,
and never went there again.

Rain, rain,
go away.
Come again
another day!

What Is the Sun?

What is the sun?
The sun is a star.

Is the sun near?
No, it is far.
What does it do?
It sends light down to you.

What is the rain?
*The rain makes
things grow.*

Like the flowers and trees?
And the rivers that flow.

By Reeve Lindbergh

Keith's Cupboard

Have you looked in Keith's cupboard?
You ought to.
You've never seen anything like
    Keith's cupboard.
Let's go over to Keith's place
and look in Keith's cupboard.

So when you get to Keith's place
you say,
"Can we play with your garage?"
And he says,
"No."

So you say,
"Can we play in your tent?"
And he says,
"No."
So you say,
"Can we play with your crane?"
And he says,
"No."

So you go up to Keith's mum
and you say,
"Can we play in Keith's tent?"
And she says,
"Keith, Keith,
why don't you get the tent out?"

"OK,"
says Keith,
and he starts going over to the cupboard –
Keith's cupboard.
He opens it, and –
Phew!

You've never seen anything like
Keith's cupboard.
In it
there's trucks, and garages, and tents
and cranes and forts and bikes and puppets
and games, and models and superhero suits
and hats and
he never plays with any of it.

They keep buying him all this stuff
and he never plays with it.

Day after day after day
it all sits in Keith's cupboard.

You ought to go over his place sometime
and have a look.
Keith's cupboard.
Phew!

By Michael Rosen

The Grand Old Duke of York

O the grand old Duke of York,
He had ten thousand men.
He marched them up to the top of the hill,
And he marched them down again.

And when they were up, they were up,
And when they were down, they were down,
And when they were only halfway up,
They were neither up nor down.

O My Grand Old Grandpa York

O My Grand Old Grandpa York
He had ten thousand teds,
He marched them into their baths every night,
Then he marched them to their beds.

And when they got in they were wet,
And when they got out they were dry,
And when they were all snuggled up very tight
He sang them a lullaby.

By Lucy Coats

The Enormous Turnip

Once upon a time there was a farmer who lived with his wife in the country.

One day the farmer planted some turnip seeds. Soon, little turnip leaves began to poke up through the soil. The farmer saw that one turnip was growing faster than the others. It grew and grew and grew until it was ENORMOUS!

"Let's have that turnip for supper tonight," said the farmer's wife. So the farmer put on his boots, walked over to the turnip patch and tried to pull the ENORMOUS turnip out of the ground.

He pulled and pulled and pulled ...

... but the turnip was stuck. So the farmer called to his wife for help.

The farmer and his wife tried to pull the **ENORMOUS** turnip out of the ground.

They pulled and pulled and pulled ...

... but the turnip was still stuck. So the farmer's wife whistled to the dog for help.

The farmer, his wife and the dog tried to pull the **ENORMOUS** turnip out of the ground.

They pulled and pulled and pulled ...

... but the turnip was still stuck.
So the dog barked to the cat for help.

The farmer, his wife, the dog and the cat tried to pull the **ENORMOUS** turnip out of the ground.

They pulled and pulled and pulled ...

... but the turnip was still stuck. So the cat mewed to a tiny mouse for help.

The farmer, his wife, the dog, the cat and the tiny mouse tried to pull the ENORMOUS turnip out of the ground.

They pulled and pulled and pulled and ...

... *whoosh!* Up came the turnip and down fell the farmer, his wife, the dog, the cat and the tiny mouse, in an ENORMOUS heap.

But nobody minded at all and they all had turnip for supper.

Retold by Karina Law

Wet Play

Wet play! Wet play!
What are we going
to do today?

Read my book,
Read my book.
That's what I shall do!

Wet play! Wet play!
What are we going
to do today?

Draw and paint,
Draw and paint.
That's what I shall do!

Wet play! Wet play!
What are we going
to do today?

Build up bricks,
Build up bricks.
That's what I shall do!

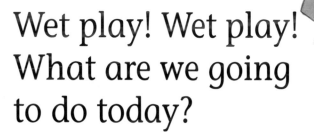

Wet play! Wet play!
What are we going
to do today?

Sit and sulk,
Sit and sulk.
That's what I shall do!

By David Orme

Way Down South

Way down South where bananas grow,
A grasshopper stepped on an elephant's toe.
The elephant said, with tears in his eyes,
"Pick on somebody your own size."

Lion

Lion, oh lion,
You don't frighten me.
You're just a big pussy cat
As anyone can see.

Lion, oh lion,
There's no need to roar.
You're not scaring anyone,
We've heard it before.

By Karina Law

Alphabet Zoo

An ant nibbled holes in my apple.
A bear bounced on my bed.
A crocodile dropped my computer,
and a donkey destroyed Dad's shed.

An elephant ate my egg.
A frog jumped into my juice.
A goat gobbled up my gloves,
and a hippo let my hamster loose.

Insects invaded my lunch box.
A jackdaw flew off with my pen.
A kangaroo stole my favourite kite,
and a lion left litter in my den.

A monkey put mud in the teapot.
A nightingale sang silly tunes.
An octopus opened our post,
and a porcupine popped my balloons.

Abba dabba doo!

A couple of quails had a quarrel.
A rabbit ran off with my car.
A skunk did stunts on my skateboard,
and a toucan took away my guitar.

A unicorn used my umbrella.
A viper had a swim in the sink.
A walrus hid in my wardrobe,
and a fox mixed worms in my drink.

A yak yelled and gave me a headache.
What a terrible hullaballoo!
A zebra had put up a sign by our house
saying, "This way to the Alphabet Zoo!"

By Karina Law

Catherine and the Lion

Catherine woke up
and saw the lion.
He was smiling.
"Hello, Lion,"
she said.

Lion walked over
and sat next to her.
Catherine told him
about her climbing
frame and her
new sister.

"Let's have
breakfast," said
Catherine. They went
downstairs.
Catherine found
an extra large
bowl for Lion.

After breakfast she went to get dressed. She decided to wear her pink dress with yellow buttons.

She put it on as quickly as she could. Then she put on her coat. "Will you come to school with me?" Catherine asked.

"Yes," said Lion. She remembered to take her library book.

At school,
she took
off her
coat and
hung it on
her peg.
"This
way," she
whispered
and went

into the classroom.
"Hello, Catherine," said Mrs Tickle.

The children were pleased to see Lion.

Catherine sat between Jason and Lauren,
and Lion sat behind her.
"Good morning, everyone," said Mrs Tickle.
"Good morning, Mrs Tickle," said the children.

In the big hall Catherine did cutting and sticking, then painting. She did a picture of Lion.

At breaktime they skipped and played, running round and round on the grass. Lion gave rides.

"I'm thirsty," said Lion. Catherine found a bowl and filled it with water for him.

After lunch everybody had a rest. They all lay on mats while Mrs Tickle read to them.

The afternoon was spent making things. Catherine made a golden crown and gave it to Lion. "Thank you, Catherine," said Lion.

When it was time to go home, Catherine gave Lion a big hug.
"I like school," she said.
"So do I," said Lion.

By Clare Jarrett

A Dark, Dark Tale

Once upon
a time there was
a dark, dark moor.
On the moor there
was a dark, dark wood.

In the wood there was a dark, dark house.
At the front of the house there was a dark,
dark door.

Behind the door there was a dark, dark hall.
In the hall there were some dark, dark stairs.

Up the stairs there was a dark, dark passage.
Across the passage was a dark, dark curtain.

Behind the curtain was a dark, dark room. In the room was a dark, dark cupboard.

In the cupboard was a dark, dark corner. In the corner was a dark, dark box.

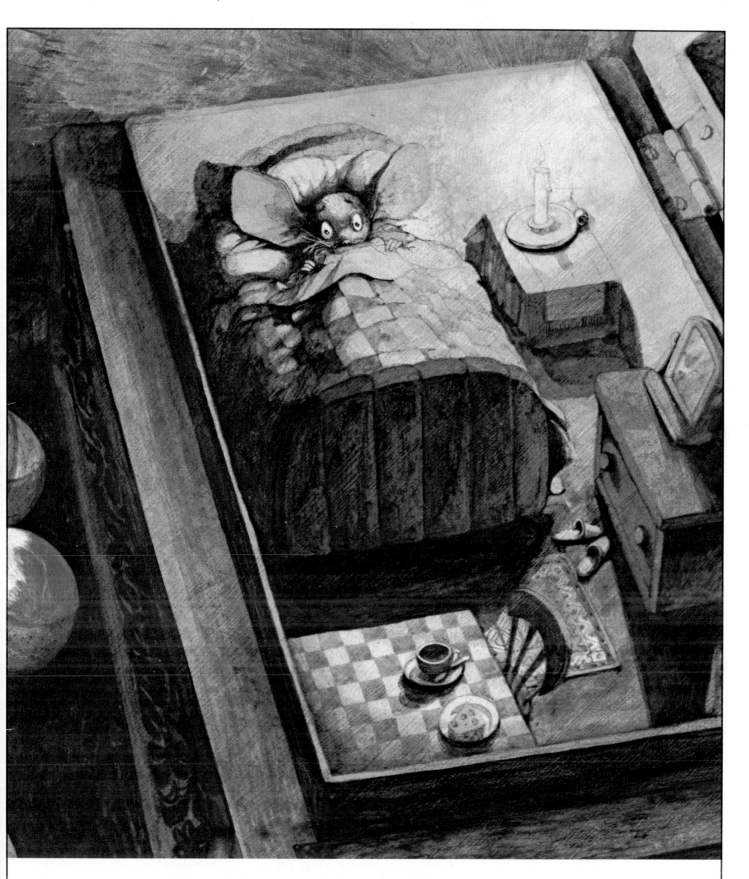

And in the box there was ... A MOUSE!

By Ruth Brown

The Baked Bean Queen

My sister would
eat baked beans
for breakfast …

… and dinner

… and tea.

She never eats anything else.
We call her "The Baked Bean Queen".

Sometimes my mum hides
sausages in the beans.

But my sister says ...

"No!"

My dad says, "Eat it for Daddy."
But my sister says ...

"No!"

I say, "I'll eat it, if you don't."
But my sister says, "Good."

So my mum says, "You'll turn into a baked bean, young lady."

And my sister says, "Good. I love baked beans."

By Rose Impey

It's Time for Lunch, Rosie!

Rosie's got her bib on,
She's got a cup and spoon,
She's sitting in her high chair –
Her lunch is coming soon!

Something very tasty,
Food she loves to eat,
Though first she has to mix it up …
And drop it on her feet!

Then she has to spread it out
And smear it on her tray,
Then she dabs it on her hair ...
And throws her spoon away!

Now her bowl is empty.
What does Rosie say?
"Food all gone! Let me out!
Rosie wants to play!"

By Tony Bradman

Night Sounds

When I lie in bed
I think I can hear
The stars being switched on
I think I can.

And I think I can hear
The moon
Breathing.

But I have to be still.
So still.
All the house is sleeping.
Except for me.

Then I think I can hear it.

By Berlie Doherty

Early Country Village Morning

Cocks crowing
Hens knowing
later they will cluck
their laying song

Houses stirring
a donkey clip-clopping
the first market bus
comes jugging along

Soon the sun will give a big yawn
and open her eye
pushing the last bit of darkness
out of the sky

By Grace Nichols

The Gingerbread Man

Once upon a time there was an old man and an old woman. One day, the old woman made a little man out of gingerbread.

She gave him currants for eyes and an orange peel mouth. Then she put him in the oven.

When the gingerbread man was baked, the old woman opened the oven door.

Suddenly, the gingerbread man jumped out of the oven and ran out of the house shouting,

**"Run! Run! As fast as you can!
You can't catch me,
I'm the Gingerbread Man!"**

The old woman called to her husband. They ran as fast as they could, but they could not catch the gingerbread man.

The gingerbread man ran and ran, and soon he met a cow. The cow said, "Moo! You look good enough to eat. Stop and let me eat you."

But the gingerbread man laughed and said,

**"Run! Run! As fast as you can!
You can't catch me,
I'm the Gingerbread Man!"**

The cow ran as fast as she could, but she could not catch the gingerbread man.

The gingerbread man ran and ran, and soon he met a horse. The horse said, "Neigh! You look good enough to eat. Stop and let me eat you."

But the gingerbread man only laughed and said,

**"Run! Run! As fast as you can!
You can't catch me,
I'm the Gingerbread Man!"**

The horse ran as fast as he could, but he could not catch the gingerbread man.

After a while the gingerbread man came to a river. A fox was prowling nearby.

The fox thought the gingerbread man looked good enough to eat, but he did not say so.

Instead he said, "Do you want to go across the river?"

"Yes, I do," said the gingerbread man.

"Jump on my back, then," said the fox, "and I will take you across."

When they were halfway across, the fox said to the gingerbread man,

"Why don't you jump up onto my head, so you don't get wet?"

So the gingerbread man did.

Then the fox said, "You might fall off my head. Why don't you jump onto the tip of my nose?"

So the gingerbread man did. The clever fox smiled a sly smile to himself, then he threw back his head and went SNAP!

And that was the end of the little gingerbread man!

Retold by Karina Law

Here a Bear, There a Bear

Here a bear, there a bear.
Everywhere there's a bear.

Bears in the hallway
Bears on the stairs

Bears under tables
Bears on chairs.

Bears in the sitting-room
Watching the telly.

Bears in the dining-room
Eating jelly.

Bears in the bathroom
Having a wash.

Bears in the kitchen
Drinking squash.

Bears in the cupboards
Bears behind doors

Bears fast asleep
On the bedroom floors.

Bears here, bears there,
There are bears everywhere.

By John Foster